Math in FOCUS®

Singapore Math®
by Marshall Cavendish

Enrichment

Consultant and Author
Dr. Fong Ho Kheong

Author
Ang Kok Cheng

 Marshall Cavendish
Education

U.S. Distributor

Houghton
Mifflin
Harcourt

© 2015 Marshall Cavendish Education Private Limited

Published by Marshall Cavendish Education
An imprint of Marshall Cavendish Education Private Limited
Times Centre, 1 New Industrial Road, Singapore 536196
Customer Service Hotline: (65) 6213 9444
U.S. Office Tel: (1-914) 332 8888 Fax: (1-914) 332 8882
E-mail: tmesales@mceducation.com
Website: www.mceducation.com

Distributed by
Houghton Mifflin Harcourt
222 Berkeley Street
Boston, MA 02116
Tel: 617-351-5000
Website: www.hmheducation.com/mathinfocus

First published 2015

Marshall Cavendish and *Math in Focus*® are registered trademarks of Times Publishing Limited.

Singapore Math® is a trademark of Singapore Math Inc and Marshall Cavendish Education Private Limited.

Math in Focus® Enrichment 4B
ISBN 978-0-544-19397-0

Printed in Singapore

1 2 3 4 5 6 7 8   1401   20 19 18 17 16 15
4500463674   A B C D E

Contents

Introducing

Math in Focus®

Enrichment

Written to complement *Math in Focus®: Singapore Math®* by *Marshall Cavendish* Grade 4, exercises in *Enrichment 4A* and *4B* are designed for advanced students seeking a challenge beyond the exercises and questions in the Student Books and Workbooks.

These exercises require children to draw on their fundamental mathematical understanding as well as recently acquired concepts and skills, combining problem-solving strategies with critical thinking skills.

Critical thinking skills enhanced by working on *Enrichment* exercises include classifying, comparing, sequencing, analyzing parts and whole, identifying patterns and relationships, induction (from specific to general), deduction (from general to specific), and spatial visualization.

One set of problems is provided for each chapter, to be assigned after the chapter has been completed. *Enrichment* exercises can be assigned while other students are working on the Chapter Review/Test, or while the class is working on subsequent chapters.

CHAPTER 7 Decimals

PROBLEM SOLVING
Thinking Skills

Write the length of $\overline{AB}$ in decimal form.

1.

A _____ B

0 cm 1 2 3 4 5 6 7 8 9 10 11 12

$AB =$ _____ cm

Study the number line and answer the questions.

P   Q   R

?   3   3.3

2. What number does point P represent?

_____

3. Round P to the nearest tenth.

_____

Compare and order the numbers.

4. Write the numbers in order from least to greatest.

6.9 $6\frac{1}{2}$ $6\frac{1}{4}$ 6.1

_____

5. Write the numbers in order from greatest to least.

7.2 $7\frac{2}{5}$ $6\frac{3}{5}$ 6.5

_____

Solve.

6. Johnson's height is 1.1 meters when rounded to the nearest tenth of a meter. What could his height be?

Fill in the blanks. Then write the missing letters in the table.
An example is shown.

7.   _0.9_ more than 6.02 is 6.92.   (C)

   a.   0.05 more than _____ is 4.73.   (E)

   b.   0.6 less than 2.98 is _____.   (M)

   c.   0.06 less than _____ is 8.27.   (L)

   d.   _____ more than 7.5 is 8.2.   (I)

   e.   0.09 more than 1.93 is _____.   (D)

   f.   0.08 less than _____ is 9.04.   (A)

   g.

Letter			C				
Number	2.02	4.68	0.9	0.7	2.38	9.12	8.33

PROBLEM SOLVING
Strategies

Complete the pattern.

8. $4\frac{1}{2}$ 5.55 $6\frac{3}{5}$ _____   _____   9.75

Solve. Show your work.

9.   Louis had a sum of money. He spent $0.75 on a notebook, 25 cents on an eraser, and $0.80 on a ruler. He had 20 cents left. How much money did Louis have at first?

10.   Paul is 0.86 meter tall. George is 0.2 meter taller than Paul but 0.05 meter shorter than Leon. How tall is Leon?

PROBLEM SOLVING
Exploration

Write each decimal in three ways.

11.   3.27 = 3 ones and 27 hundredths

      = _____

      = _____

      = _____

12.   4.587 = 4 ones and 5 tenths 8 hundredths 7 thousandths

      = _____

      = _____

      = _____

Solve.

13.   Five decimals form a pattern when arranged in order.
Three of these decimals are shown below.
Find all possible pairs of decimals to form a pattern.

| 0.69 | 0.80 | | | 0.58 |

Journal Writing

The statements below are incorrect. Write the correct statements.

14. In 14.238, the value of the digit 1 is ten, and the value of the digit 3 is tenth.

_____

15. 2.409 is the same as 2 ones and 4 tenths 9 hundredths.

_____

16. 9.3 more than 0.2 is the same as 9.3 > 0.2.

_____

Find the rule for each number pattern. Then complete the pattern.

17. 0.42   0.53   0.64   _____   _____

Rule: _____

18. 7.95   7.71   7.47   _____   _____

Rule: _____

19. 0.06   0.12   0.24   _____   _____

Rule: _____

Adding and Subtracting Decimals

PROBLEM SOLVING

Thinking Skills

Solve.

1. Each letter stands for a different digit. Find the digit that each letter stands for. Use the digits 1, 2, 3, and 5.

    $$A.CB + B.BC = C.DD$$

2. The sum of the numbers on each side of the triangle is 13.2. Fill in the circles with the given decimals.

    1.2   2.4   3.6   4.8   6   7.2

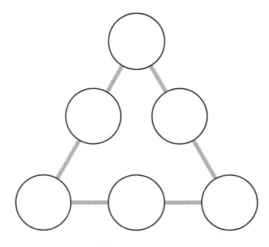

Name: _____   Date: _____

Solve. Show your work.

3.   The table shows the fees for the hotel parking garage.
Mr. Spencer parked his car from 1:00 P.M. to 5:14 P.M.
How much did Mr. Spencer have to pay to park his car?

Schedule	Charges
1:00 P.M. to 5:00 P.M.	$2.50 an hour or part of an hour
After 5:00 P.M.	$4.00 an hour or part of an hour

4.   Lee spent $4.30 on a plate of spaghetti, $1.25 on a bottle of
fruit juice, and $3.45 on a fountain pen. Lee had $50 at first.
How much money was she left with?

Solve. Show your work.

Mrs. Kemery bought some canned food from a shop. She bought one can of each type of food. The table shows the prices of the canned food.

Canned Food	Price (one can)
Fruit Cocktail	$3.50
Condensed Milk	95¢
Tuna	$2.32
Pineapple	$11.27

5. How much cheaper is a can of tuna than a can of fruit cocktail?

6. Mrs. Kemery bought an extra can of pineapple and a can of fruit cocktail. How much did Mrs. Kemery spend altogether?

PROBLEM SOLVING
Strategies

Solve. Show your work.

7.   Morgan saved $3.85 on Friday.
He saved $2.20 more on Saturday than on Friday.
The amount Morgan saved on Sunday was equal to the total amount
of money he saved on both Friday and Saturday.
How much did Morgan save altogether on Saturday and Sunday?

8.   Mrs. Blaine had 0.95 pound of chicken in the fridge, but she decided to
buy some more. She used 2.75 pounds of chicken to make some stew and
minced 1.42 pounds of chicken for a Shepherd's pie. She was left with
1.35 pounds of chicken. How much chicken did Mrs. Blaine buy?

9. Natalie is 1.32 meters tall.
Her younger brother Eric is 0.38 meter shorter than she is.
Their father is 0.45 meter taller than Natalie.
What is the total height of the three of them?

PROBLEM SOLVING
Exploration

Solve.

10.   Find all possible values of A, B, and C. Each letter stands for a different digit.

```
    0. C A
  + 0. 2 B
  ---------
    1. 0 1
```

11.   Find all possible values of X, Y, and Z. Each letter stands for a different digit.

```
    1. X Y
  - 0. Z 9
  ---------
    0. 6 1
```

Journal Writing

Number the steps in the correct order.

12.   Write 1, 2, 3, and 4 in the boxes to show the steps for adding
the two decimals.

$$
\begin{array}{r}
0.\ 5\ 6 \\
+\ \ 0.\ 7\ 3 \\
\hline
1.\ 2\ 9 \\
\end{array}
$$

☐   Add the ones.

☐   Regroup the tenths.

☐   Add the tenths.

☐   Add the hundredths.
No regrouping is required.

Name: _____   Date: _____

Write the steps.

13. Write the steps needed to add the six decimals.

0.83 + 0.17 + 0.45 + 0.55 + 0.96 + 0.04

Step 1 _____

_____

_____

Step 2 _____

_____

_____

Step 3 _____

_____

_____

Step 4 _____

_____

_____

Write the steps.

14.   Write the steps needed to subtract the decimals.

$$
\begin{array}{r}
1.\ 4\ 7 \\
-\ 0.\ 9\ 8 \\
\hline
0.\ 4\ 9
\end{array}
$$

Step 1   _____

_____

_____

Step 2   _____

_____

_____

Step 3   _____

_____

_____

Step 4   _____

_____

9 Angles

PROBLEM SOLVING

Thinking Skills

Solve.

1. How many more angles measuring less than 90° are there in Figure A than in Figure B?

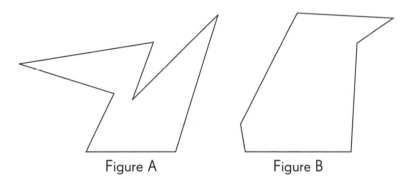

Figure A   Figure B

2. Measure and list the angles in order from the smallest angle to the largest angle.

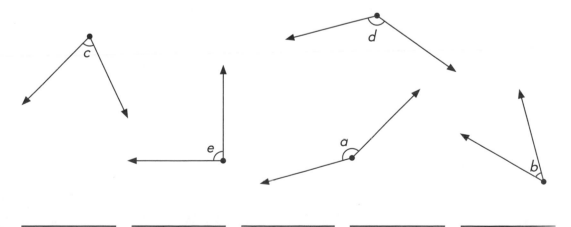

_____ _____ _____ _____ _____

Smallest   Largest

Solve. Show your work.

3. Mary started her piano lesson at 5:20 P.M. The lesson ended at 7:05 P.M. How many $\frac{1}{4}$-turns did the minute hand of the clock move through during this time?

Solve. Show your work.

4.   Use a protractor to draw an angle that is one right angle greater than $\angle w$. Label the angle as $\angle AOC$. What is the measure of this new angle?

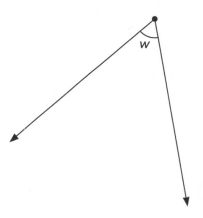

5. $\overleftrightarrow{AB}$ is a line. Draw an angle, $\angle COD$, that has a measure of 125°. The measure of $\angle AOC$ is 30°. What is the measure of $\angle DOB$?

PROBLEM SOLVING
Strategies

Solve.

6. The measure of angle *A* is twice as great as the measure of angle *B*, and the measure of angle *C* is 3 times the measure of angle *B*. The measure of angle *D* is half of the measure of angle *C*, and the measure of angle *A* is 36° greater than the measure of angle *B*. Find the measure of angle *D*.

Draw.

7. After turning $\frac{3}{4}$-turn clockwise, $1\frac{1}{2}$-turns counterclockwise, and then another $\frac{1}{4}$-turn clockwise, the arrow rests in this final position.

Draw the original position of the arrow.

8. The angle *k* below is made up of angles *a*, *b*, *c*, and *d*. What is angle *d*?

PROBLEM SOLVING

Exploration

Solve.

9. Arjun is facing north. He wants to end up facing west. Arjun can only use $\frac{1}{2}$-turns, $\frac{1}{4}$-turns, and $\frac{3}{4}$-turns. List three ways that Arjun can turn to end up facing west.

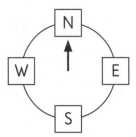

Think of turning once, twice, or three times, and of turning in different directions.

a. _____

b. _____

c. _____

10. Find the measure of the unknown angle with the help of a protractor. Describe the method you used to find the angle measure.

_____

_____

Journal Writing

Number the steps in the correct order. Then draw the angle.

11.   Write 1, 2, 3, and 4 in the boxes to show the steps for drawing
a 145° angle. Then draw a 145° angle in the space provided.

☐   Place the base line of the protractor on the line and the center
of the base line on the point.

☐   Remove the protractor. Draw a ray from the point on the line
to the dot.

☐   Use the outer scale to find the 145° mark. Mark it with a dot.

☐   Draw a line and mark a point on the line.

Write a short description.

12. Describe how you can get from point *A* to point *K* on the grid below.

Use $\frac{1}{4}$-turn, $\frac{1}{2}$-turn, and $\frac{3}{4}$-turn in your description.

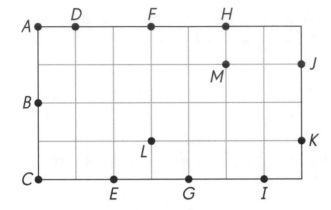

_____

_____

_____

_____

_____

_____

_____

CHAPTER 10 Perpendicular and Parallel Line Segments

PROBLEM SOLVING
Thinking Skills

Answer the questions.

1. Which letters have a set of perpendicular line segments?

   A   H   K   L   U   O   E   F

2. Which letters have a set of parallel line segments?

   Y   P   S   I   M   W   Q   H

Study the figure carefully and use it to do Exercises 3 to 5.

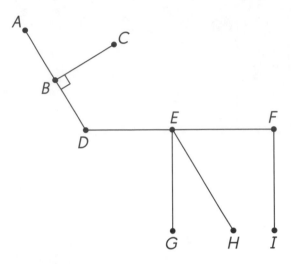

3. $\overline{AD}$ is most likely parallel to _____.

4. Put a cross (**✗**) beside the statements that are false.

   a. $\overline{AB} \parallel \overline{CB}$ _____

   b. $\overline{DF} \perp \overline{EG}$ _____

   c. $\overline{EH} \perp \overline{AD}$ _____

   d. $\overline{EG} \parallel \overline{IF}$ _____

5. What is the total number of pairs of parallel line segments that can be found in the figure?

Draw.

6. Caroline wants to divide the rectangle into 4 identical right triangles and a square using 2 pairs of parallel line segments. Draw the 2 pairs of parallel line segments to show how she can do this.

7. Benjamin has a rectangular picture.
He wants to frame it with a rectangular frame.
In the figure, 2 sides of the frame have been drawn.
Complete the frame by drawing the remaining 2 line segments accurately.

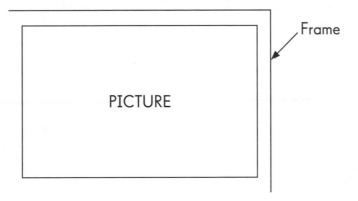

Draw.

8. Use a drawing triangle and a straightedge to draw a line segment parallel to $\overline{AB}$ at point C. Then draw another line segment parallel to $\overline{BC}$ at point A. Extend each line segment until they meet. Label the point of intersection D.

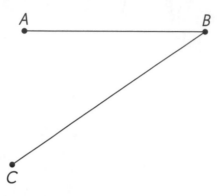

9. The figure is made up of two identical 4-centimeter squares overlapping each other. Draw the figure to scale in the space provided.

Name: _____   Date: _____

PROBLEM SOLVING
Strategies

Answer the questions.

10. The figures below are arranged in a pattern.
    How many horizontal and vertical line segments will there be in figure D7 altogether?

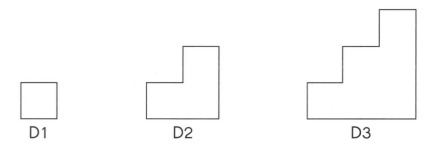

D1   D2   D3

11. Figure A is drawn using 2 horizontal and 5 vertical line segments. Figure B is drawn using 3 horizontal and 2 vertical line segments. There are 9 figures altogether with a total of 21 horizontal and 36 vertical line segments. How many figure As are there?

PROBLEM SOLVING

Exploration

Draw.

12.   Draw as many squares as possible. Use $\overline{AB}$ as one side of each square. How many squares can you draw?

Draw.

13.   Draw four rectangles. Use $\overline{AB}$ as one side of each rectangle.

Draw.

14. Draw six squares. Use each side of the right triangle as a side for two squares.

Name: _____ **Date:** _____

Journal Writing

Explain.

15. Explain how you would draw a line segment parallel to $\overline{BC}$ and a line segment perpendicular to $\overline{BC}$.

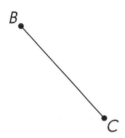

Parallel line segment:

_____

_____

_____

_____

Perpendicular line segment:

_____

_____

_____

_____

Describe.

16. Describe this shape using the words *parallel* and *perpendicular*.

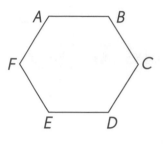

_____

_____

_____

17. Think of a shape with 5 sides or more. Draw the shape and describe it using the words *parallel* and *perpendicular*.

_____

_____

_____

Squares and Rectangles

PROBLEM SOLVING

Thinking Skills

Solve. Show your work.

1. The figure is made up of 9 identical rectangles.
The length of each identical rectangle is twice its width.
Find the perimeter of two of these identical rectangles.

96 cm

Solve. Show your work.

2.   The figure below is made up of rectangle *ABCD* and square *EFGH*.
EC = *CH*. Find the total length of $\overline{BE}$, $\overline{EF}$, and $\overline{CH}$.

3.   A school wants to fence its field. The fence will run along the sides
and the back of the tool shed. The length of the tool shed is one-third
the length of the field, and the width of the tool shed is one-quarter the
width of the field. How many meters of fencing, excluding a 4-meter gate,
must the school order?

gate

Solve. Show your work.

4. The perimeter of rectangle *ABCD* is twice the perimeter of square *EFGH*.
    What is the length of rectangle *ABCD*?
    The figures are not drawn to scale.

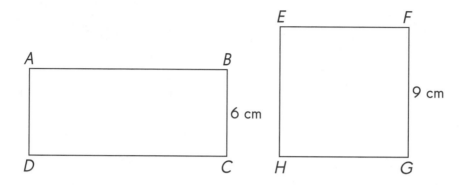

5. The figure is made up of 5 squares. Each side of square A is 6 centimeters
    long, each side of square B is 4 centimeters long, and each side of square
    C is 5 centimeters long. Find the total length around the figure.

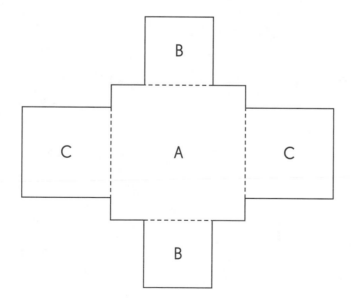

Solve. Show your work.

6. The figure shows three identical squares.
    Find the sum of the measures of $\angle a$ and $\angle b$.

Strategies

Solve. Show your work.

7.   Figure *ABCD* is a square. The measure of ∠*a* is twice the measure
of ∠*b*. Find the measure of ∠*a*.

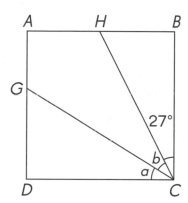

8.   The figure, not drawn to scale, is a square. The measure of ∠*c* is half
of the measure of ∠*a*. The measure of ∠*b* is 20° less than the measure of ∠*a*.
Find the sum of the measures of ∠*a* and ∠*b*.

PROBLEM SOLVING
Exploration

Solve.

9.   Find the total number of rectangles and the total number of squares in the figure.

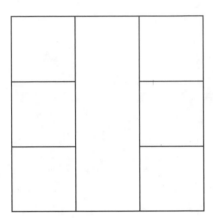

10.   Trace and cut out the squares and rectangles below. Use the cut-outs to make 4 different figures.

Answer the question.

11. Draw 2 line segments in each rectangle so that each line segment touches any two sides of the rectangle. Mark all the angles. How many angles are there in each case?

Journal Writing

Compare.

12. Write down all the properties of squares and rectangles.
Compare them and circle the common properties.

Square	Rectangle
_____	_____
_____	_____
_____	_____
_____	_____
_____	_____
_____	_____
_____	_____
_____	_____
_____	_____

List the steps.

13. The figure is made up of line segments that meet at right angles. Write the steps you used to find the lengths of $\overline{GH}$ and $\overline{DE}$.

CHAPTER 12 Conversion of Measurements

PROBLEM SOLVING
Thinking Skills

Solve.

1.   Victoria sprinted 90 meters. What was the distance in centimeters?

Read the scale.

2.   If each can of corn has the same mass, what will be the mass of two such cans in grams?

3.   Express the volume of water in the jug in milliliters.

4.   Emma finds the mass of a bag and a chair. She finds that the bag has a mass of 6 kilograms 9 grams. Both the chair and the bag have the same mass. Color the boxes that show the mass of the chair.

6,090 g	6,900 g	6,009 g

6 kg 9 g	6 kg 900 g	6 kg 90 g

5. A jug contains 3 liters 500 milliliters of water. Water from the jug is used to fill seven 250-milliliter mugs. Find the amount of water left in the jug.

6. Convert each measurement to liters and milliliters. Then shade the boxes with the two largest and the two smallest measurements.

Y	S	O	E
1,903 mL	6,012 mL	3,250 mL	7,009 mL
____ L ____ mL	____ L ____ mL	____ L ____ mL	____ L ____ mL

J	T	D	R
300 mL	1 mL	4,020 mL	1,025 mL
____ L ____ mL	____ L ____ mL	____ L ____ mL	____ L ____ mL

A	I	U	M
5,001 mL	8,150 mL	6,905 mL	250 mL
____ L ____ mL	____ L ____ mL	____ L ____ mL	____ L ____ mL

Arrange the letters in the shaded boxes to spell out the answer to the following riddle.

What can fly without wings?

_____ _____ _____ _____

PROBLEM SOLVING

Strategies

7.   Look for the pattern.

10 cm   1 m 15 cm   _____   3 m 40 cm   _____

8.   At a charity walk, Bryan walks 3 kilometers 320 meters more than Luis. Kerry walks 850 meters less than Bryan. Luis walks 6 kilometers. Find the total distance walked by Kerry and Bryan.

9. A pail contains a certain amount of water. After Peter used it to fill a 1.5 liter can, a 750 milliliter bottle, and a 2 liter 250 milliliter tin, he realized that he had a liter of water left in the pail. How much water was in the pail at first?

PROBLEM SOLVING
Exploration

10. The total mass of two goats is 48 kilograms. The mass of one of the goats is at least 10 kilograms more than the other. The mass of the lighter goat is more than 16 kilograms. Find three possible masses of the heavier goat.

Journal Writing

Correct the mistakes.

11. 2 km 5 cm = 2 × 100 cm + 5 cm = 205 cm

_____

_____

12. 4,050 g = 40 kg 50 g

_____

_____

13. 750 mL = 7 L 50 mL

_____

_____

CHAPTER 13   Area and Perimeter

PROBLEM SOLVING
Thinking Skills

Solve. Show your work.

1. Each edge of a cube is 9 centimeters long.
Find the total length of all the edges of the cube.

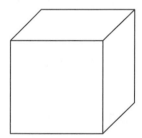

2. A rectangle has a perimeter of 140 centimeters. Its length is 4 times its width. Find the area of the rectangle.

Solve. Show your work.

3. Jack needs to run a distance of 800 meters around a rectangular field. The field is 65 meters long and 15 meters wide. How many times must Jack run around the field?

4. The figure below is not drawn to scale. *ABCD* and *EFGC* are rectangles, and *GHIC* is a square. *BE = EC*. Find the perimeter of the whole figure.

Solve. Show your work.

5.   A rectangular piece of paper measures 13 centimeters by 9 centimeters.
Estimate the number of squares, each with a side length of 4 centimeters,
that can be cut from the piece of paper.

6.   The figure below is made up of 6 identical rectangles.
Each of these identical rectangles has a width that is half its length.
The area of the figure is 768 square centimeters.
Find the perimeter of one of the six rectangles.

PROBLEM SOLVING
Strategies

Solve. Show your work.

7.   The length of a rectangle was 6 times its width. When the length was
increased by 6 centimeters, the area became 36 square centimeters.
Then, when the width was increased by 4 centimeters, the new width
became 6 centimeters. What was the perimeter of the rectangle at first?

8.   The area of rectangle B is half of the area of rectangle A.
The width of A is two-thirds its length.
The width of B is three-quarters its length.
The width of A is the same as the length of B, and the area of A is between
60 square centimeters and 100 square centimeters.
Find the lengths of both rectangles.

Solve. Show your work.

9.   The figure is made up of squares of different sizes.
The side length of each square is half the side length of the next square.
The area of square A is 9 square centimeters.
What is the perimeter of the largest square?

PROBLEM SOLVING
Exploration

Answer the questions.

Use a geoboard and a rubber band. Make as many figures as you can that have an area of 12 square centimeters. Find the length, width, and perimeter of each figure. Record the lengths, widths, and perimeters in the table.
If you do not have a geoboard, you can use grids. Shade the different figures on separate grids.

Figure	1	2	3	4	5	6
Area	12	12	12	12	12	12
Length						
Width						
Perimeter						

10. What is the minimum perimeter of the figures you have made? Can you make another figure with a smaller perimeter?

11. What is the maximum perimeter of the figures you have made? Can you make another figure with a larger perimeter?

12. Describe any pattern you observe.

13.   In each figure, draw line segments to divide the figure into squares or rectangles. Each line segment should touch at least one corner of the figure. Number the shapes you have identified.

a.

b.

Journal Writing

Write the steps.

14. Find the perimeter of the figure. Write the steps you use to find the perimeter.

15. The outer rectangle is 48 centimeters long and 24 centimeters wide.
The path around the inner rectangle is 3 centimeters wide.
Find the area of the inner rectangle.
Write the steps you use to find the area.

CHAPTER 14 Symmetry

PROBLEM SOLVING
Thinking Skills

Solve.

1. Draw a line of symmetry on the figure.

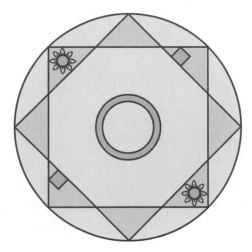

2. All sides of the figure are equal in length. How many lines of symmetry are there in the figure?

Shade.

3.   The figure is made up of 25 squares. Shade 5 more squares so that the figure has 4 lines of symmetry.

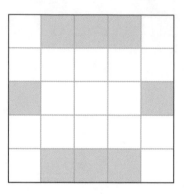

4.   Shade the figures that have rotational symmetry and at least one line of symmetry.

Answer the question.

5.   How many letters in each of these words have rotational symmetry and
     line symmetry?

UNITED   STATES   OF   AMERICA

_____   _____   ____   _____

Draw.

6.   Gillian folds a piece of paper and cuts out a shape as shown.
     Draw the shape when the paper is unfolded.

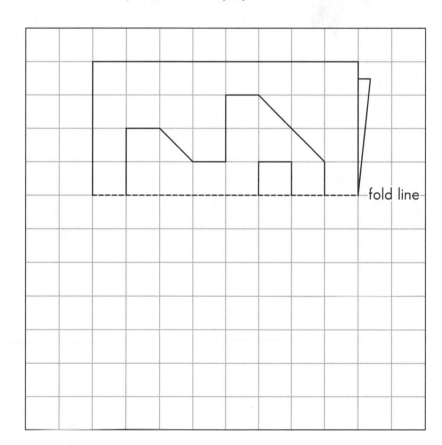

fold line

Shade and draw.

7. Shade 9 squares so that the figure has a line of symmetry.
Draw the line of symmetry.

PROBLEM SOLVING
Strategies

Solve.

8. After rotating a $\frac{1}{4}$-turn counterclockwise, a $\frac{3}{4}$-turn clockwise, and

another $\frac{1}{2}$-turn clockwise about point O, figure A rests in this final position.

Draw the original position of figure A.

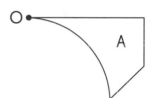

9. Felicia is making a pattern using symmetric shapes.
She has made three designs.
How many squares will she need to make the fifth design?

First   Second   Third

PROBLEM SOLVING

Exploration

10. **a.** Draw 2 figures that are congruent to the shape.

 b. Draw 2 figures that are not congruent to the shape.

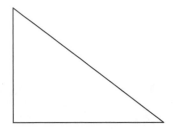

11. Shade squares so that the dotted line becomes a line of symmetry.

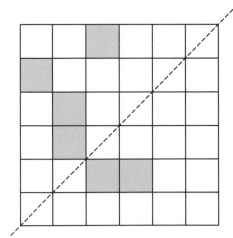

Draw.

12. Jack and Jade play a game. Jack starts by drawing a square on a grid. Jade continues by drawing the least number of squares needed to make the next symmetric figure. They take turns drawing the next symmetric figure. Draw the possible symmetric figures they could draw at each stage.

13. In the next game, Jade begins with a triangle. Draw the possible symmetric figures they could draw at each stage.

© Marshall Cavendish International (Singapore) Private Limited.

Draw.

14. Draw 3 figures that have rotational symmetry.

Journal Writing

15. Explain why the statements are wrong.

a. The figure shows a flip.

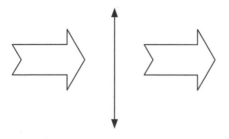

b. The figure shows a rotation.

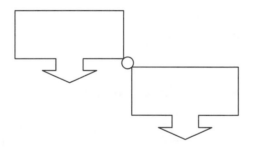

c. The figure shows a slide.

16.   Explain why the pair of figures are not congruent.

a.

b.

Write the steps.

17.   The figure shows only half of a symmetric shape.
Write the steps needed to complete the symmetric figure.

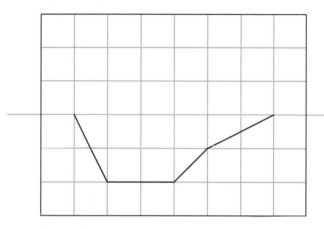

Step 1   _____

_____

Step 2   _____

_____

Step 3   _____

_____

Step 4   _____

_____

Write the steps.

18. The figure shows a symmetric shape. Write the steps used to find a line of symmetry.

Step 1 _____

_____

Step 2 _____

_____

Step 3 _____

_____

Step 4 _____

_____

Tessellations

CHAPTER 15

PROBLEM SOLVING

Thinking Skills

Solve.

1. Mr. Carter wants to put tiles of only one shape in his bathroom.
The tiles must fit together so that there are no gaps in between them.
Which of the following shapes can Mr. Carter use?

2.   Use the shape to make a tessellation in the space provided.

3.   Use the shape to make a tessellation in the space provided.

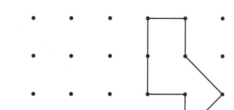

4.   Use the shape to make four different tessellations in the space provided.

a.   Tessellation 1

b. Tessellation 2

c. Tessellation 3

d. Tessellation 4

5. The tessellation was formed using Unit Shape A. Identify and outline all the unit shapes within the tessellation.

Unit Shape A

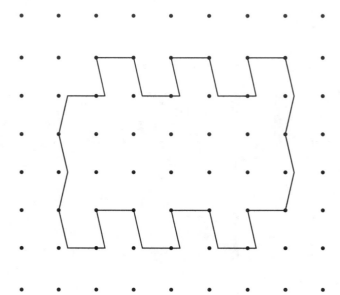

Solve.

6. Charlie has a rectangular plot of land. He wants to divide his land equally among his eight children. The first figure below shows the shape of the plot of land each child will receive. On the grid, show how Charlie should distribute the land among his children.

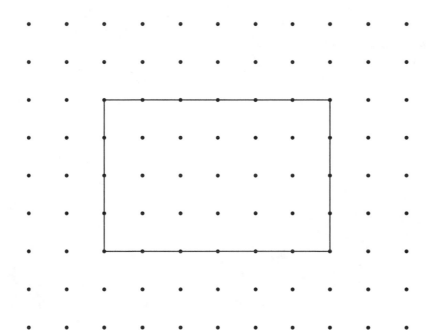

© Marshall Cavendish International (Singapore) Private Limited.

PROBLEM SOLVING
Strategies

Answer the questions.

7.   John uses matchsticks to make a tessellation.

   a.   How many matchsticks will he need to form figure S6?

   b.   Which figure is formed with 125 matchsticks?

S1   S2   S3   S4

Solve. Show your work.

8.   A tessellation was made from toothpicks. After some unit shapes were removed from the tessellation, the tessellation was left with the unit shapes shown. How many toothpicks were used to form the original tessellation?

PROBLEM SOLVING
Exploration

Tessellate the shape in two different ways.

9.

Tessellation 1

Tessellation 2

Tessellate the shape in two different ways.

10.

Tessellation 1

Tessellation 2

Tessellate the shape in two different ways.

11.

Tessellation 1

Tessellation 2

Journal Writing

Explain.

12.   Explain why the shape does not tessellate when used in figure A but does
tessellate when used in figure B.

A

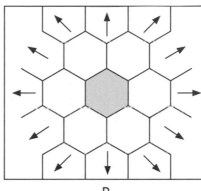

B

_____

_____

_____

13.   The first shape is a parallelogram that can tessellate.
Explain how you can form the second shape, which can also tessellate, from
the first shape.

 →

_____

_____

_____

Answers

Chapter 7

1. Solution: 10.7

2. Thinking skill: Deduction

   Solution: 2.85

3. Solution: 2.9

4. Thinking skills: Comparing, Sequencing

   Solution: 6.1, $6\frac{1}{4}$, $6\frac{1}{2}$, 6.9

5. Thinking skills: Comparing, Sequencing

   Solution: $7\frac{2}{5}$, 7.2, $6\frac{3}{5}$, 6.5

6. Thinking skill: Identifying patterns and relationships

   Solution: Accept answers ranging from 1.05 meters to 1.14 meters.

7. Thinking skill: Comparing

   Solution:

   a. 0.05 more than <u>4.68</u> is 4.73.
   b. 0.6 less than 2.98 is <u>2.38</u>.
   c. 0.06 less than <u>8.33</u> is 8.27.
   d. <u>0.7</u> more than 7.5 is 8.2.
   e. 0.09 more than 1.93 is <u>2.02</u>.
   f. 0.08 less than <u>9.12</u> is 9.04.
   g.

D	E	C	I	M	A	L
2.02	4.68	0.9	0.7	2.38	9.12	8.33

8. Strategy: Look for patterns

   Solution: 7.65, $8\frac{7}{10}$

9. Strategy: Work backward

   Solution:
   20 cents more than $0.80 is $1.
   25 cents more than $1 is $1.25.
   75 cents more than $1.25 is $2.
   Louis had $2 at first.

10. Strategy: Use a diagram

    Solution:
    0.2 more than 0.86 = 1.06
    0.05 more than 1.06 = 1.11
    Leon is 1.11 meters tall.

11. 3 ones and 2 tenths 7 hundredths
    32 tenths and 7 hundredths
    327 hundredths

12. 4 ones and 5 tenths 7 hundredths
    17 thousandths
    4 ones and 4 tenths 18 hundredths
    7 thousandths
    3 ones and 15 tenths 8 hundredths
    7 thousandths

13. 0.58, 0.69, 0.80, <u>0.91</u>, <u>1.02</u>;
    <u>0.36</u>, <u>0.47</u>, 0.58, 0.69, 0.80;
    <u>0.47</u>, 0.58, 0.69, 0.80, <u>0.91</u>

14. In 14.238, the value of the digit 1 is 1 ten, and the value of the digit 3 is 3 hundredths.

15. 2.409 is the same as 2 ones and 4 tenths 9 thousandths.

16. Answers vary. Samples: 9.3 more than 0.2 is different from 9.3 > 0.2.
    9.3 more than 0.2 is the same as 9.3 + 0.2.

17. 0.75; 0.86
    Add 0.11 to each decimal.

18. 7.23; 6.99
    Subtract 0.24 from each decimal.

19. 0.48; 0.96
    Multiply each decimal by 2.

Chapter 8

1. Thinking skills: Analyzing parts and whole, Identifying patterns and relationships

   Solution: A = 1; B = 2; C = 3; D = 5
   1.32 + 2.23 = 3.55

2. Thinking skills: Comparing, Analyzing parts and whole, Identifying patterns and relationships

   Solution:

   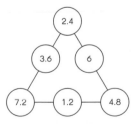

3. Thinking skills: Classifying, Analyzing parts and whole

   Solution:
   $2.50 + $2.50 + $2.50 + $2.50 + $4.00 = $14.00
   Mr. Spencer had to pay $14.00 to park his car.

4. Thinking skill: Analyzing parts and whole
   Solution:
   $50 − $4.30 − $1.25 − $3.45 = $41
   She had $41 left.

5. Thinking skill: Comparing
   Solution:
   $3.50 − $2.32 = $1.18
   A can of tuna is $1.18 cheaper than a can of fruit cocktail.

6. Thinking skill: Analyzing parts and whole
   Solution:
   $3.50 + $3.50 + $0.95 + $2.32 + $11.27 + $11.27 = $32.81
   Mrs. Kemery spent $32.81 altogether.

7. Strategy: Use a model
   Solution:

   Friday: $3.85
   Saturday: $3.85 + $2.20 = $6.05
   Sunday: $3.85 + $6.05 = $9.90
   $6.05 + $9.90 = $15.95
   Morgan saved $15.95 altogether on Saturday and Sunday.

8. Strategy: Work backward
   Solution:
   2.75 + 1.42 + 1.35 − 0.95 = 4.57
   Mrs. Blaine bought 4.57 pounds of chicken.

9. Strategy: Use a diagram
   Solution:

   Eric: 1.32 − 0.38 = 0.94
   Father: 1.32 + 0.45 = 1.77
   1.32 + 0.94 + 1.77 = 4.03
   The total height of the three of them is 4.03 meters.

10. A = 0; B = 1; C = 8
    A = 1; B = 0; C = 8
    A = 2; B = 9; C = 7
    A = 3; B = 8; C = 7
    A = 5; B = 6; C = 7
    A = 6; B = 5; C = 7
    A = 8; B = 3; C = 7
    A = 9; B = 2; C = 7
    If the sum of A and B is 1, then C must be 8.
    If the sum of A and B is 11, then C must be 7.

11. X = 1; Y = 0; Z = 4
    X = 2; Y = 0; Z = 5
    X = 3; Y = 0; Z = 6
    X = 4; Y = 0; Z = 7
    X = 5; Y = 0; Z = 8
    X = 6; Y = 0; Z = 9
    To get 1 in the hundredths place, the value of Y must be 0.
    X and Z always have a difference of 3, with X < Z.

12. 1 – Add the hundredths.
       No regrouping is required.
    2 – Add the tenths.
    3 – Regroup the tenths.
    4 – Add the ones.

13. **Step 1:** Write the numbers in vertical form. Line up the decimal points.
    Step 2: Add the hundredths.
       Regroup the hundredths.
       3 + 7 + 5 + 5 + 6 + 4
       = 30 hundredths
       = 3 tenths
    Step 3: Add the tenths.
       Regroup the tenths.
       8 + 1 + 4 + 5 + 9 + 0 + 3
       = 30 tenths = 3 ones
    Step 4: Add the ones.
       0 + 0 + 0 + 0 + 0 + 0 + 3
       = 3 ones

14. **Step 1:** Regroup 4 tenths 7 hundredths.
       4 tenths 7 hundredths
       = 3 tenths 17 hundredths
    Step 2: Subtract the hundredths.
       17 − 8 = 9
    Step 3: Regroup 1 one and 3 tenths.
       1 one and 3 tenths
       = 13 tenths
    Step 4: Subtract the tenths.
       13 tenths − 9 tenths = 4 tenths

Chapter 9

1. Thinking skills: Comparing, Spatial visualization

   Solution:

   Figure A: 4; Figure B: 1

   $4 - 1 = 3$

   There are 3 more angles.

2. Thinking skills: Comparing, Sequencing

   Solution:

   $\angle b$ (45°), $\angle c$ (70°), $\angle e$ (90°), $\angle d$ (130°), $\angle a$ (150°)

3. Thinking skill: Spatial visualization

   Solution:

   $1\frac{1}{4}$-turn: 15 minutes

   5.20 P.M. to 6.05 P.M.: $3\frac{1}{4}$-turns

   6.05 P.M. to 7.05 P.M.: $4\frac{1}{4}$-turns

   So, the total is $7\frac{1}{4}$-turns.

   The minute hand moved through $7\frac{1}{4}$-turns during this time.

4. Thinking skill: Comparing

   Solution:

   $90° + 60° = 150°$

   The measure of the new angle drawn is 150°.

5. Thinking skill: Analyzing parts and whole

   Solution:

   $180° - 30° - 125° = 25°$

   The measure of $\angle DOB$ is 25°.

6. Strategy: Use a model

   Solution:

   $36° \times 3 = 108°$

   $108° \div 2 = 54°$

   The measure of angle D is 54°.

7. Strategy: Work backward

   Solution:

8. $\angle a = 72°$, $\angle b = 56°$, $\angle c = 116°$

   $\angle d = 41°$

9. Answers vary. Samples:

   $\frac{1}{4}$-turn counterclockwise;

   $\frac{1}{2}$-turn counterclockwise followed by

   $\frac{1}{4}$-turn clockwise;

   $\frac{1}{2}$-turn clockwise followed by $\frac{3}{4}$-turn

   counterclockwise

10. 235°

    Methods for finding the angle measure vary.

    Sample:

    Extend one ray to cut the angle into two smaller angles. Measure each angle. The sum of the two angle measures is the unknown angle measure.

11. 2; 4; 3; 1

12. Answers vary.

    Sample:

    Move from point A to point F, make a $\frac{1}{4}$-turn

    clockwise, move from point F to point L, make

    a $\frac{1}{4}$-turn counterclockwise, move from point L

    to point K.

Chapter 10

1. Thinking skill: Use a diagram

   Solution: H L E F

2. Thinking skill: Use a diagram

   Solution: I M W H

3. Thinking skill: Comparing

   Solution: $\overline{EH}$

4. Thinking skill: Comparing

   Solution: a; c

5. Thinking skill: Comparing

   Solution: 2

6. Thinking skill: Spatial visualization

   Solution:

7. Thinking skill: Spatial visualization

Solution:

8. Thinking skill: Spatial visualization

Solution:

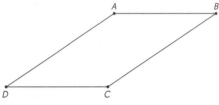

9. Thinking skill: Spatial visualization

Solution:

Check that the students draw the correct figure.

10. Strategy: Look for patterns

Solution: 16

D1 – 4

D2 – 6

D3 – 8

D4 – 10

D5 – 12

D6 – 14

D7 – 16

11. Strategy: Guess and check

Solution: 6

Figure	No.	HL	VL	9 Figures?	21 HL?	36 VL?
A B	3 6	6 18	15 12	yes	no	no
A B	5 4	10 12	25 8	yes	no	no
A B	6 3	12 9	30 6	yes	yes	yes

12. 2 squares

13. Answers vary. Sample:

14.

15. Parallel line segments:

Place a drawing triangle against $\overline{BC}$.
Then place a straightedge at the base of
the drawing triangle.
Slide the drawing triangle along the
straightedge.
Use the edge of the drawing triangle to
draw $\overline{DE}$.
$\overline{BC}$ and $\overline{DE}$ are parallel.

Perpendicular line segments:

Mark a point on $\overline{BC}$ and label it D.
Place the center of the baseline of the protractor
on point D.
Mark a point at the 90° mark and label it E.
Use the edge of the protractor to connect point
E and point D.
$\overline{BC}$ and $\overline{DE}$ are perpendicular.

16. The shape has three pairs of parallel sides: $\overline{AB}$ and $\overline{ED}$, $\overline{BC}$ and $\overline{FE}$, $\overline{AF}$ and $\overline{CD}$. It has no perpendicular sides.

17. Answers vary.

Chapter 11

1. Thinking skills: Analyzing parts and whole, Identifying patterns and relationships

    Solution:
    Width = 96 ÷ 6 = 16 cm
    Perimeter of 1 rectangle = 6 × 16 = 96 cm
    Perimeter of 2 rectangles = 2 × 96 = 192 cm

2. Thinking skill: Analyzing parts and whole

    Solution:
    Length of $\overline{EC}$ = Length of $\overline{CH}$ = 3 cm
    Length of $\overline{BE}$ = 18 − 3 = 15 cm
    Total = 15 + 6 + 3 = 24 cm
    The total length is 24 cm.

3. Thinking skill: Analyzing parts and whole

    Solution:
    Length of tool shed = 54 ÷ 3 = 18 m
    Width of tool shed = 28 ÷ 4 = 7 m
    Total length of fencing
    = 54 + 54 + 28 + 28 + 7 + 7 − 4
    = 174 m
    The school must order 174 meters of fencing.

4. Thinking skill: Analyzing parts and whole

    Solution:
    Perimeter of square EFGH
    = 4 × 9 = 36 cm
    Perimeter of rectangle ABCD
    = 2 × 36 = 72 cm
    Length of $\overline{AB}$ = (72 − 6 − 6) ÷ 2 = 30 cm

5. Thinking skill: Analyzing parts and whole

    Solution:
    Total = 2 × 15 + 4 × 1 + 2 × 12 + 4 × 2
    = 30 + 4 + 24 + 8
    = 66 cm
    The total length is 60 centimeters.

6. Thinking skill: Spatial visualization

    Solution:
    90° − 25° = 65°
    2 × 65° = 130°
    The sum of the measures is 130°.

7. Strategy: Use a diagram

    Solution:
    90° − 27° = 63°
    63° ÷ 3 = 21°
    ∠a = 2 × 21° = 42°

8. Strategy: Use a model

    Solution:

    90° + 20° = 110°
    110° ÷ 5 = 22°
    a → 2 × 22° = 44°
    b → 44° − 20° = 24°
    44° + 24° = 68°
    The sum of the measures is 68°.

9. 16 rectangles; 7 squares

10. Answers vary. Sample:

    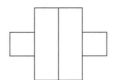

11. Answers vary. Sample figures:

    12 angles

    16 angles

    12 angles

    16 angles

12. Properties of a square:
    • All sides have equal length.
    • (Opposite sides are parallel.)
    • (All angles measure 90°.)
    Properties of a rectangle:
    • Opposite sides have equal length.
    • (Opposite sides are parallel.)
    • (All angles measure 90°.)

13. $GH + AB = FE + DC$
$GH + 5$ cm $= 7$ cm $+ 1$ cm
$GH + 5$ cm $= 8$ cm
$GH = 3$ cm
$AH + GF = BC + DE$
5 cm $+ 3$ cm $= 1$ cm $+ DE$
8 cm $= 1$ cm $+ DE$
$DE = 7$ cm

Chapter 12

1. $90 \times 100 = 9000$ cm.

2. 4 kg ➞ 4000 g
$\dfrac{4000}{5} \times 2 = 1600$ g

3. Thinking skill: Comparing
Solution:
1,700 mL

4. Thinking skill: Comparing
Solution:
6,009 g; 6 kg 9 g

5. Thinking skill: Analyzing parts and whole
Solution:
Amount of water poured into the mugs:
250 mL $\times 7 = 1,750$ mL
3,500 mL $- 1,750$ mL $= 1,750$ mL
$= 1$ L 750 mL

Amount of water left in the jug is 1 liter 750 milliliters.

6. Thinking skills: Comparing, Sequencing
Solution:

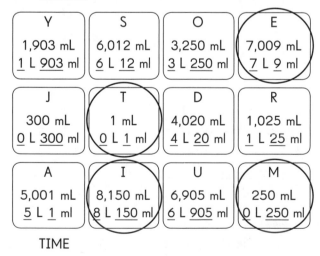

Y	S	O	E
1,903 mL	6,012 mL	3,250 mL	7,009 mL
1 L 903 ml	6 L 12 ml	3 L 250 ml	7 L 9 ml

J	T	D	R
300 mL	1 mL	4,020 mL	1,025 mL
0 L 300 ml	0 L 1 ml	4 L 20 ml	1 L 25 ml

A	I	U	M
5,001 mL	8,150 mL	6,905 mL	250 mL
5 L 1 ml	8 L 150 ml	6 L 905 ml	0 L 250 ml

TIME

7. 2 m 25 cm   4 m 60 cm

8. Strategy: Use a model
Solution:

Distance walked by Bryan:
6 km $+ 3$ km 320 m $= 9$ km 320 m
Distance walked by Kerry:
9 km 320 m $- 850$ m $= 8$ km 470 m
Distance walked by Bryan and Kerry:
9 km 320 m $+ 8$ km 470 m $= 17$ km 790 m

9. $1.5 + 0.75 + 2.25 + 1$
$= 4.5$ L / 4 L 500 mL / 4,500 mL.

10. $48 - 10 = 38$
$38 \div 2 = 19$
$19 + 10 = 29$
The heavier goat is at least 29 kg.
Since the mass of the lighter goat is more than 16 kg, three possible masses of the heavier goat are 29 kg, 30 kg, or 31 kg.

11. 2 km 5 cm $= 2 \times 1,000 \times 100$ cm $+ 5$ cm
$= 200,000$ cm $+ 5$ cm
$= 200,005$ cm

12. 4,050 g $= 4$ kg 50 g

13. 750 mL $= 0$ L 750 mL

Chapter 13

1. Thinking skill: Spatial visualization
Solution:
$12 \times 9 = 108$
The total length of all the edges of the cube is 108 centimeters.

2. Thinking skill: Identifying patterns and relationships
Solution:
10 units ➞ 140 cm
1 unit ➞ 14 cm
Length $= 4 \times 14 = 56$ cm
Width $= 14$ cm
Area $= 56 \times 14 = 784$ cm^2

© Marshall Cavendish International (Singapore) Private Limited.

3. Thinking skill: Analyzing parts and whole

Solution:

Once around the field = 65 + 65 + 15 + 15
$$= 160 \text{ meters}$$

$800 \div 160 = 5$

Jack must run around the field 5 times.

4. Thinking skill: Analyzing parts and whole

Solution:

Perimeter = 28 + 14 + 6 + 6 + 6 + 14
$$+ 6 + 14 + 14 = 108 \text{ cm}$$

5. Thinking skills: Analyzing parts and whole,
   Identifying patterns and
   relationships

Solution:

$13 \div 4$ is about 3.

$9 \div 4$ is about 2.

$3 \times 2 = 6$

About 6 squares can be cut from the piece of paper.

6. Thinking skills: Analyzing parts and whole,
   Identifying patterns and
   relationships

Solution:

$768 \div 6 = 128$

$16 \times 8 = 128$

Perimeter = 16 + 8 + 16 + 8 = 48 cm

7. Strategy: Work backward

Solution:

$6 - 4 = 2$

$36 \div 2 = 18$

$18 - 6 = 12$

Perimeter = 12 + 2 + 12 + 2 = 28 cm

8. Strategy: Guess and check

Solution:

Length of rectangle A = 12 cm

Length of rectangle B = 8 cm

A			B			Area of A between 60 and 100 cm²?
L	W	A	L	W	A	
6	4	24	4	3	12	no
9	6	54	6	$4\frac{1}{2}$	27	no
12	8	96	8	6	48	yes

9. Strategy: Look for patterns

Solution:

$9 = 3 \times 3$

$3 \times 2 = 6$

$6 \times 2 = 12$

$12 \times 2 = 24$

$4 \times 24 = 96$

The perimeter of the largest square is 96 centimeters.

10. 14 cm; no

Figure	1	2	3	4	5	6
Area	12	12	12	12	12	12
Length	12	6	4	—	—	—
Width	1	2	3	—	—	—
Perimeter	26	16	14	—	—	—

11. 26 cm; no

12. With the same area, the greater the length of a figure, the greater its perimeter.

13. Answers vary. Sample:

a.

b.

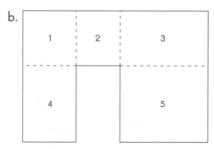

14. $AF = BC + DE = 7$ cm

$EF = AB + CD = 21$ cm

Perimeter = 7 + 21 + 7 + 21 = 56 cm

15. $48 - 3 - 3 = 42$

$24 - 3 - 3 = 18$

$42 \times 18 = 756$

The area of the inner rectangle is 756 square centimeters.

Chapter 14

1. Thinking skill: Spatial visualization
   Solution:

   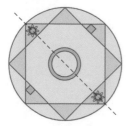

2. Thinking skill: Spatial visualization
   Solution: 8

3. Thinking skill: Spatial visualization
   Solution:

   Answers vary. Sample:

4. Thinking skill: Spatial visualization
   Solution:

5. Thinking skills: Classifying, Spatial visualization
   Solution: 1 (I); 0; 1 (O); 1 (I)

6. Thinking skills: Identifying patterns and relationships, Spatial visualization
   Solution:

   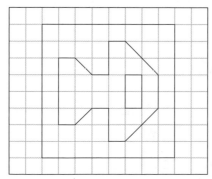

7. Thinking skill: Spatial visualization
   Solution:

   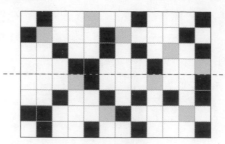

8. Strategy: Work backward
   Solution:

9. Strategy: Look for patterns
   Solution: 15 squares
   First — 1
   Second — 3
   Third — 6
   Fourth — 10
   Fifth — 15

10. a. Answers vary.
    Accept all figures that have the same shape and size.

    b. Answers vary.
    Accept all figures that have a different shape and/or size.

11.

12. Answers vary. Samples:

13. Answers vary. Samples:

14. Answers vary. Samples:

15. a. Both the shapes are facing the same direction.
It is a slide, not a flip.

   b. The shape has changed position but it still
faces the same direction.
It is a slide, not a rotation.

   c. The shapes are facing different directions.
It is a rotation, not a slide.

16. a. They are not the same shape or the same size.

   b. They are not the same size.

17.

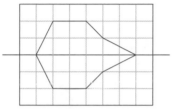

   Step 1: Identify the line of symmetry.

   Step 2: Look at the existing part of the figure
and study it in relation to the line of
symmetry.

   Step 3: Draw lines above the line of symmetry
that are congruent to the lower half of
the drawing.

   Step 4: Continue drawing until you have
completed the symmetric figure.

18. **Step 1:** Copy the figure on a sheet of paper
and cut it out.

   Step 2: Draw a line across the figure.

   Step 3: Fold the figure along this line.

   Step 4: Check if the two parts are congruent and
match exactly. If they do, then the line
you have drawn is a line of symmetry.

Chapter 15

1. Thinking skills: Identifying patterns and
relationships, Spatial visualization
Solution: A, B, C, and D are all possible.

2. Thinking skills: Identifying patterns and
relationships, Spatial visualization
Solution:

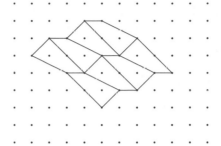

3. Thinking skills: Identifying patterns and
relationships, Spatial visualization

   Solution:

4. Thinking skills: Identifying patterns and
relationships, Spatial visualization

   Solution: Answers vary. Samples:

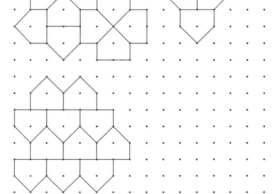

5. Thinking skills: Identifying patterns and
                     relationships, Spatial visualization

    Solution:

6. Thinking skills: Identifying patterns and
                     relationships, Spatial visualization

    Solution: Answers vary. Sample:

7. Strategy: Look for patterns

    Solution:

    a. 13 (This is a + 2 pattern.)
       3 + 2 + 2 + 2 + 2 + 2 = 13
       He will need 13 matchsticks to form figure S6.
    b. 125 − 1 = 124
       124 ÷ 2 = 62
       Figure S62 is formed with 125 matchsticks.

8. Strategy: Simplify the problem

    Solution:

    6 toothpicks form a hexagon.
    There are 7 hexagons in half of the pattern.
    6 × 7 = 42
    12 of the toothpicks are shared between the
    hexagons.
    42 − 12 = 30
    There are 2 groups of 7 hexagons in the pat-
    tern.
    2 × 30 = 60
    3 of the toothpicks are shared between the 2
    groups of 7 hexagons.
    60 − 3 = 57
    57 toothpicks were used to form the original
    tessellation.

9. Answers vary. Samples:

10. Answers vary. Sample:

11. Answers vary. Sample:

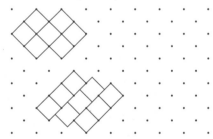

12. In figure A, the shape does not tessellate
    because there are gaps between the figures.
    In figure B, the shape tessellates because it
    covers a surface with no gaps or overlaps
    between the figures.

13. Cut a triangle on the left end of the
    parallelogram and move it to the right end.